WRITING
MATHEMATICS

NANCY ROGERS BOSSE

Grade **3**

By reading the bar graph I discovered three interesting things about myself. First I learned that 3 other people like to play handball. Second I learned that I am t... kid in my class that... Bird. Lastly I lear... that 11 other peopl... have brown hair.

Creative Publications

Creative Publications, MathLand, LinkerCubes, Fractions Squares PLUS, and Fractions Circles PLUS are all trademarks or registered trademarks of Creative Publications.

Edited by Rhea Irvine
Cover and text designed by Hyru Gau
Illustrations edited by Fred Geier
Coordinated by Theresa Tomlin
Composition by William Seabright & Associates

Thanks to the teachers and students who tried out these activities. Their writing can be seen on pages iv-xi of this book.

© 1995 Creative Publications
1300 Villa Street
Mountain View, California 94041

Printed in the United States of America
ISBN: 1-56107-823-9
1 2 3 4 5 6 7 8 9 10 99 98 97 96 95

Table of Contents

- Dear Reader
- Paragraph Format
- 1-cm Grid
- 1-inch Grid
- Pentomino Puzzles
- Report Format
- Editing Checklist
- Game Boards
- Editing Experts

Notes to the Teacher

"To know mathematics is to engage in a quest to understand and communicate."

NCTM Curriculum and Evaluation Standards for School Mathematics

WHAT IS *WRITING MATHEMATICS?*

Writing Mathematics is a series of resource books for grades one through six. Each book offers ten lessons designed to help students develop oral and written language as tools for learning and communicating mathematical ideas.

The key elements of the lessons ensure the active, social participation of students; the use of students' natural language and intuitive understandings; the connection of everyday language to the language of mathematics; and the development of students as writers of informal and structured expository writing. *Writing Mathematics* provides model experiences which can be incorporated throughout your mathematics program.

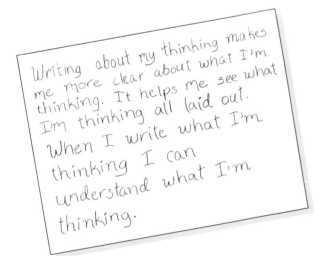

Writing about my thinking makes me more clear about what I'm thinking. It helps me see what I'm thinking all laid out. When I write what I'm thinking I can understand what I'm thinking.

HOW IS *WRITING MATHEMATICS* ORGANIZED?

Included in *Writing Mathematics* are ten multi-day lessons which connect writing experiences to the investigation of key mathematical ideas.

The four-page guide to each lesson includes an overview; plans for the math investigation and writing extension, assessment criteria, and ideas for promoting discourse.

Use the Table of Contents to weave the *Writing Mathematics* lessons into your math outline for the year, or use the chart on page 1 to see how the lessons are intended to be used with *MathLand.*

WHAT ABOUT MANIPULATIVES?

The *Writing Mathematics* Manipulative Kit for Grade Three (Cat. No 31853) includes the following materials:

1600 Rainbow Cubes in 7 colors
16 sets Fraction Circles PLUS
80 orange Rainbow Tiles
32 Numeral Dice in 2 colors
Animals of the Zoo Cards
Fraction Squares PLUS for the
    Overhead Projector

You may wish to have students or volunteers help with the preparation of manipulatives and classroom supplies prior to a lesson.

A Look Inside a Classroom

In this classroom, the students were engaged in the first lesson, *Getting to Know You*. The mathematics investigation focused on collecting, communicating, and interpreting data. The students first invented questions to ask their classmates about their interests and preferences. Then the students predicted the results, surveyed their peers to collect the actual data, and organized and displayed their data on bar graphs. Finally, the class discussed the results of the surveys and how the results compared to their earlier predictions.

In the writing extension, students again interpreted data from the graphs, this time for a different purpose and using a new method. The students first took notes from the graphs, then organized their notes to write a structured expository paragraph which included a topic sentence and three or four supporting sentences. The teacher used the overhead projector to model the new writing skills introduced in this extension. (See pages 2-5 for the complete lesson description.)

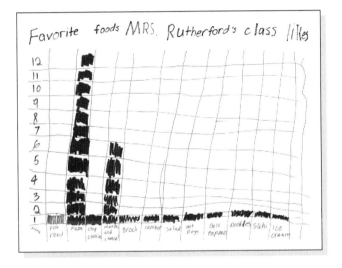

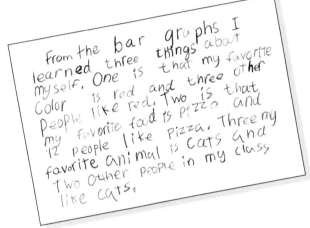

A WORD ABOUT
WRITING TO LEARN

To learn mathematics, students must construct it for themselves. Constructing meaning engages students in many processes, including exploring, predicting, describing, and justifying. Writing to report experiences, relate findings, and explain thinking challenges students to use these same processes.

As students write to make sense of mathematics, they become aware of what they know and do not know. The motivation to increase their understanding is the product of their own process of making meaning. Awareness of their misconceptions helps students clarify their understandings, while consolidation of their understandings allows students to make connections and extend their thinking.

As students explain and apply their understandings, teachers gain important insights into their students' approaches to and uses of mathematics.

"Math is a language that needs to be spoken; a music that needs to be heard; and an art that needs to be seen."

Rachel McAnallen

THE MATH INVESTIGATION

During the math sessions of *Getting to Know You,* students worked in pairs. Beginning the investigation with the opportunity for students to generate their own questions for surveying the class established the students' ownership of the undertaking. They went to work enthusiastically, predicting the results and conducting their surveys. Conversations about decisions to be made and how to proceed filled the room as pairs worked side by side organizing and displaying their data.

Throughout the investigation, the teacher observed, questioned, and listened as each student brought something unique to the exploration. The teacher was free to interact with students, challenging them to think in new ways and gathering information about their thinking : *Tell me about what you are doing. Is it working? Is this what you expected? Now what will you do?*

WRITING MATHEMATICS • GRADE 3

THE WRITING EXTENSION

Students naturally had a great interest in learning about themselves in relation to the rest of their class. Using note taking as a method for collecting information from the graphs was an interesting challenge. Notice in the examples below how one student used key words while the other relied on more complete sentences.

Using the notes they collected, students were then challenged to write a paragraph describing what they learned about themselves in relation to the rest of the class. Because this writing activity was done early in the year and students were not familiar with topic and supporting sentences or transition words, modeling and much discussion was needed.

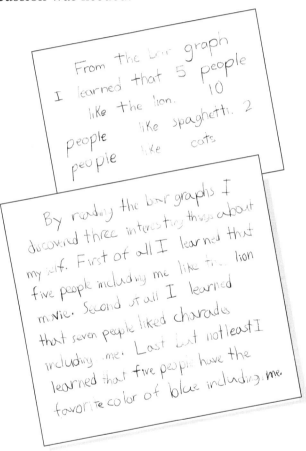

From the bar graph I learned that 5 people like the lion. 10 people like spaghetti. 2 people like cats

By reading the bar graphs I discovered three interesting things about myself. First of all I learned that five people including me like the lion movie. Second of all I learned that seven people liked charades including me. Last but not least I learned that five people have the favorite color of blue including me.

10 people like spaghetti.

5 coler blue

5 like the lion.

5 lion move

2 people like cats.

11 broWn hiar

7 ch a rads

These finished drafts show the range in the children's products. Notice that the first writer did not communicate what she learned about herself in relation to the rest of the class. The second writer incorporates transition words, and the paragraph flows nicely. Both drafts provide the teacher with important information that can be used to plan further math and writing experiences.

A NOTE FROM A TEACHER

As expected at this early point of the year, most of my students had a difficult time articulating a topic sentence and writing two or three supporting sentences. At first I was hesitant to provide a writing format, fearing that such a structure would stifle the students' writing. Instead, I found that providing the format allowed my students to focus on the primary thinking involved in the task and have a structure for expressing their ideas. Their natural language still came through using the structure. In addition, I appreciated having the model to give me added direction as to the writing format. I realized my students need a lot of prewriting experience, language development, and discussion to get started, and prompts and encouragement in large doses.

I've already begun to use this writing format in other subject areas. In reading, I had the students choose one character from our story and write a topic sentence and two or three supporting sentences about one characteristic of that character. I was pleased to see how much more natural the students' writing was and how much more comfortable they were with the format.

A WORD ABOUT
LEARNING TO WRITE

Throughout *Writing Mathematics*, students are engaged in the writing process. They produce finished products for specific purposes and audiences, as well as write informally in journals.

Prewriting activities include investigating mathematics, holding discussions, and brainstorming. At the writing stage, students are presented with a structure with which to experiment as they write rough drafts. The variety of formats introduced support students as they write to explain, convince, describe, compare, plan, and report.

The revision and editing stages involve students in rereading and rethinking the presentation of their ideas. Modeling, conferencing, peer editing, and using editing checklists and editing roles help students approach this stage with confidence. Finally, the publication stage provides ways for students to use their writing for its planned purposes.

Initially, you will want to take students through the lessons step-by-step. As students become familiar with the writing process, they will work more independently and intermix stages of the writing process, revising as they draft, for example.

Another Look Inside a Classroom

In this classroom, students were engaged in the mathematics and writing lesson, *Odd and Even Tops*. The math investigation challenged students to extend the pattern created when even and odd numbers were shown with Rainbow Cubes. Students worked in pairs to make predictions and confirm their theories about the results of adding different combinations of even and odd numbers. As they worked, they recorded their findings.

In the writing extension, students wrote persuasive paragraphs intended to convince someone else that their theories about odd and even numbers were correct. The format for the expository paragraph was revisited with an emphasis on presenting procedures and examples. Students took their explanations home to be read by a family member. (See pages 6-9 for the complete lesson description.)

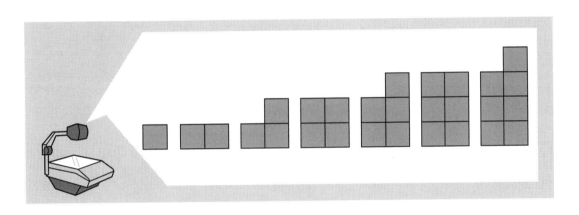

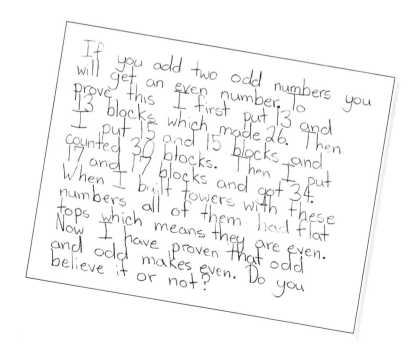

If you add two odd numbers you will get an even number. To prove this I first put 13 and 13 blocks which made 26. Then I put 15 and 15 blocks and counted 30 blocks. Then I put 17 and 17 blocks and got 34. When I built towers with these numbers all of them had flat tops which means they are even. Now I have proven that odd and odd makes even. Do you believe it or not?

A WORD ABOUT
CLASSROOM TALK

Classroom Talk, a feature appearing at the end of each lesson, touches upon the rationale for emphasizing oral language in the mathematics and writing curriculum, and provides helpful suggestions for promoting discourse in the classroom. Topics such as the role of silence in discourse, journal conversations, the link between oral language and writing, and the development of mathematical vocabulary are addressed.

Reading through all the *Classroom Talk* columns prior to beginning *Writing Mathematics* is recommended; the suggestions provided are applicable throughout the program.

"Probing questions that encourage children to think and explain their thinking orally and in writing help them to understand more clearly the ideas they are expressing."

NCTM Curriculum and
Evaluation Standards for
School Mathematics

THE MATH INVESTIGATION

To introduce the math sessions of *Odd and Even Tops*, the teacher placed Rainbow Cubes on the overhead projector in a pattern showing even and odd numbers. She challenged her students to identify and continue the pattern of the cubes. Much discussion ensued as the students tried to make sense of the pattern. Identification of the pattern progressed from a *block pattern* to *a counting pattern* and finally to *a pattern of even and odd numbers*.

Following the whole class discussion, students worked in pairs to explore the results of adding different combinations of odd and even numbers. Using Rainbow Cubes, making sketches, and arriving at their own findings made this investigation meaningful to students.

THE WRITING EXTENSION

Students were then challenged to use their thinking and recordings from the math activity to write an expository paragraph convincing someone else that one of their theories about the sum of odd and even numbers was correct.

Partners were first asked to write down their procedures and provide some examples of number combinations they investigated. The student's notes shown below were sufficient for developing the complete and well-structured paragraph shown at right.

Prior to having students begin their individual writing, the teacher talked with the class about possible topic and concluding sentences, transition words to use when describing procedures, and ways to introduce examples. Attention was given to the flow of an expository paragraph.

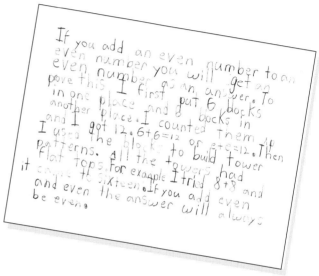

In the paragraph above, the student has used the writing format effectively to communicate his understanding and theory about adding even numbers. Notice the way he uses transition words to make his writing flow smoothly from one idea to the next.

A NOTE FROM A TEACHER

My class enjoyed doing the math and the writing lesson, and I feel the students learned from their experiences. I was especially pleased that the students continued their own investigations of odd and even patterns. Several students looked at bigger numbers to see if they could determine if they were odd or even. A couple of students wanted to see if they could write a theory about the results of subtracting combinations of odd and even numbers. These are the kinds of connections that show me that learning has taken place.

Because my group this year is composed of many poor readers and emergent writers, the paragraph format was particularly challenging. I can see that my students will need many more opportunities to practice writing an expository paragraph before they feel comfortable with the format.

A WORD ABOUT ASSESSMENT

Each lesson provides questions to think about while evaluating students' writing. The questions focus first on the students' thinking about mathematics and, second, on the students' use of the writing process and writing formats to communicate their ideas. You may wish to use the questions as the framework for an assessment rubric.

The writing process provides many opportunities for self-assessment. Students reflect on their writing and use the responses of peers to evaluate and revise their writing. As students hear how classmates have written, they have still another opportunity to reconsider the writing they have done.

To *MathLand* Teachers

Writing Mathematics is designed to supplement the complete *MathLand* mathematics program. Teachers using *MathLand* already create mathematical environments which encourage students to think, to invent, to investigate, and to make connections.

Writing Mathematics provides exemplary writing extensions which add to the student writing about thinking, journaling, and self-assessment in *MathLand*. Some of the writing extensions are opportunities to takeoff from a *MathLand* investigation, while others provide a format for students to use as they do the writing called for within a *MathLand* investigation. Together, these experiences provide a rich program of learning to write and writing to learn.

The ten math investigations in *Writing Mathematics* provide synopses of investigations in the *MathLand* program. *MathLand* teachers will want to use the complete plans presented in the guidebook. It may be helpful to note in your guidebook the point of use for each writing extension, as shown in the chart below.

The techniques and writing formats provided in *Writing Mathematics* are intended to be used to extend other *MathLand* investigations; revisit these experiences as appropriate for your class.

Teachers not yet using *MathLand* and interested in this unique mathematics program are invited to call 800-357-MATH for information.

The *MathLand* • *Writing Mathematics* Correlation				
MathLand			**Writing Mathematics**	
Unit 1	Week 1	Pages 6 - 11	Getting to Know You	Pages 2 - 5
Unit 2	Week 2	Pages 40 - 41	Odd and Even Tops	Pages 6 - 9
Unit 3	Week 3	Pages 70 - 77	Convince Me!	Pages 10 - 13
Unit 4	Week 4	Pages 118 - 125	The Giant Chart	Pages 14 - 17
Unit 5	Week 1	Pages 150 - 155	Crazy Creatures	Pages 18 - 21
Unit 6	Week 5	Pages 206 - 211	Fraction Images	Pages 22 - 25
Unit 7	Week 1	Pages 222 - 227	Measuring Around	Pages 26 - 29
Unit 8	Week 1	Page 259	Pentomino Search	Pages 30 - 33
Unit 9	Week 1	Pages 286 - 293	Animal Research	Pages 34 - 37
Unit 10	Week 1	Pages 334 - 341	Tally Ho!	Pages 38 - 41

Getting to Know You

MATHEMATICS FOCUS

Interpreting Data

A bar graph is one effective way to organize and report data. Counting and displaying data is helpful in comparing data.

Students survey each other about personal interests and preferences. They record, organize, and display in bar graphs the data, then talk about what they can learn about each other from the graphs.

....

MATERIALS

❑ full and eighth sheets of paper

❑ chart paper

❑ 12" x 18" drawing paper
   For each pair

❑ 1 envelope

PREPARATION Make a copy of your class roster for each pair.

TIME 2 sessions

WRITING FOCUS

Describing Ourselves

Taking notes is an effective way to collect and organize data from graphs. A good descriptive paragraph has a topic sentence and three or four supporting sentences.

Students interpret bar graphs in order to gather information about themselves. They take notes, then write and edit an organized paragraph which is used in a guessing game.

....

MATERIALS

❑ note cards, at least 4 for each student

❑ writing paper

PREPARATION The bar graphs from the math sessions should be posted around the room. Prior to class time, take your own notes from the graphs on a transparency and cut them to note card size.

TIME 1-2 sessions

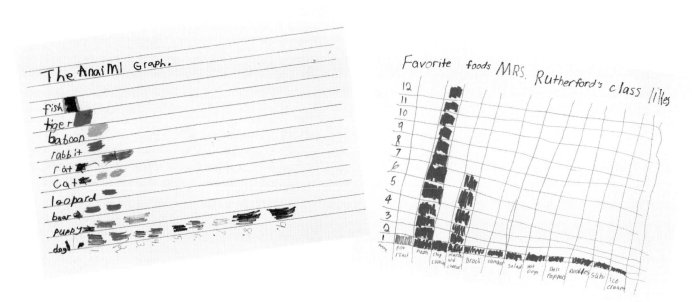

Interpreting Data

*We spend some time getting to know each other. Then we display
what we have learned on bar graphs.*

TAKING SURVEYS

1 *We're going to take some surveys to get to know each
other.* Brainstorm questions students could ask each
other. For example:

- *How many are in your family?*
- *What is a movie you like?*
- *What kind of cereal do you like best?*
- *What is your favorite food?*

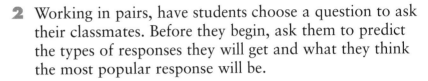

2 Working in pairs, have students choose a question to ask
their classmates. Before they begin, ask them to predict
the types of responses they will get and what they think
the most popular response will be.

3 For their survey, the pairs use a class roster, note each
person's response on a separate slip of paper, and collect
all of the responses in an envelope. Remind students to
respond to their own survey question.

**DISPLAYING
OUR DATA**

4 Have students organize the data they have collected and
display the results on a bar graph.

> The graphs should have three things: a title, words to tell what
> the bars mean, and numbers so it's easy to tell how many in
> each bar. Beyond this, let students make their own choices
> about how to organize their work, rather than giving them a
> preset structure.

5 When the graphs are complete, discuss how the results
compare with the students' predictions.

- *What was the most popular response?*
- *Were you able to predict it?*
- *What surprised you about the results of your survey?*

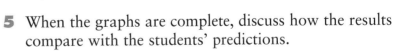

Describing Ourselves

We use the information collected from our graphs to write paragraphs which include the clues for a guessing game.

TAKING NOTES

1 *Now let's use our graphs to learn more about ourselves and each other.* Tell students they will collect information from the graphs, then write paragraphs containing clues that describe themselves. Later, one student will read an unidentified paragraph, while the rest of the class tries to guess who the paragraph describes.

2 *First, look at the graphs and think about what they tell you about yourself in relation to the rest of the class.* Explain to students they will write their paragraphs when they return to their seats, so they should take notes to help them remember what they find. Model note-taking strategies. Refer to Classroom Talk.

3 Provide students with note cards and have them take at least four notes from the graphs.

WRITING TO DESCRIBE

4 Have students look at their note cards and choose the three most interesting facts to include in their paragraphs. *Put those cards in the order you want for your paragraph.*

5 *A good paragraph has a topic sentence and at least three or four supporting sentences. A topic sentence tells the reader what the paragraph is going to be about.* Ask students to suggest topic sentences, and write the suggestions on the board. Model using your own notes to write a paragraph. Talk through your thinking process as you write, then have students write first drafts.

> Help students understand that writing is a process. Point out that this is the stage for taking the ideas in their notes and organizing them into cohesive paragraphs. Encourage students not to concern themselves with spelling, mechanics, or neatness at this point. Later they will have time to edit for these things.

TOPIC SENTENCES

- From the bar graphs I learned...

- By reading the bar graphs, I discovered three interesting things about myself.

- Our bar graphs are one way to see how I compare to others. For instance, I learned...

CREATING AN EDITING CHECKLIST

6 Before the paragraphs are read for the guessing game, have students reread their writing and revise. *What are some things you should look for as you revise?* Write the students' responses on chart paper to create an editing checklist.

> As students create the checklist, you will get a glimpse of their understanding of revision and editing. As the year progresses, steps can be added to this list. When the list is long, have students circle three things to focus on in each writing activity.

WHO AM I?

7 Select a student to read a paragraph aloud. Students should try to guess the author of the paragraph, citing evidence from the graphs.

ASSESSMENT

To assess this writing activity, evaluate how well the students communicate what they know about interpreting data in one-paragraph descriptions of themselves.

- *Did the student take accurate notes from the graphs?*
- *Does the paragraph include a topic sentence and three supporting facts or details?*

(Classroom Talk)

MODELING

Modeling is an effective teaching strategy when introducing new skills. Writing and thinking out loud in front of the class allows students to construct the meaning and importance of writing. In addition, modeling allows the teacher to experience the thinking involved in the writing experience.

In this lesson, model note-taking strategies. Prior to class time, take your own notes from the graphs on a transparency and cut them to note card size. Display them on the overhead projector.

Here are the notes I took about myself from the graphs.

Notice that I used one card for each fact I discovered. Talk about each note card.

- *Are these complete sentences?* Encourage the students to write only key words and phrases.
- *What do you think I meant by these words (or this phrase)?*
- *From which graph do you think I got this information?*

Odd and Even Tops

MATHEMATICS FOCUS

Discovering Patterns

All numbers that are not even are odd, and every whole number fits into one of these categories. All even numbers make a Rainbow Cube configuration that the odd numbers cannot make.

Students examine the pattern created when even and odd numbers are shown with Rainbow Cubes. They make predictions and confirm their theories about the results of adding combinations of odd and even numbers.

••••••••••••••••••••••••••••••••••••••

MATERIALS

    For each pair

❑ 100 Rainbow Cubes in one color

❑ full sheets of paper

PREPARATION Have an overhead projector and Rainbow Tiles set up. Be ready to show the pattern on page 7.

TIME 1 session

WRITING FOCUS

Convincing Readers

The structure of a persuasive paragraph is effective for explaining our thinking about odd and even numbers. In a persuasive paragraph, supporting sentences should include a procedure and examples.

Students write persuasive paragraphs, explaining procedures and providing examples to convince someone else that their theories about odd and even numbers are correct. The paragraphs are read by people outside the class.

••••••••••••••••••••••••••••••••••••••

MATERIALS

❑ writing paper

❑ chart paper

PREPARATION Make a copy for each student of Dear Reader (page 42). Make a transparency of Paragraph Format (page 43).

TIME 1-2 sessions

Discovering Patterns

We investigate odd and even numbers and develop theories about the results of adding them.

EXTENDING A PATTERN

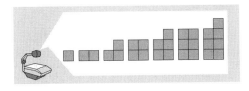

1 *To start, let's look at this pattern of numbers.* On the overhead projector, begin the pattern shown at left, using the tiles. ***When you see the pattern I am making, work with your partner to continue the pattern to 12 using Rainbow Cubes.***

2 When students have finished their patterns, have a class discussion about what they discovered.

- *Tell me what you notice about the pattern.*
- *If we made numbers to 1000, do you think we'd find one that didn't fit the pattern? Why or why not?*
- *Let's give this pattern a name.*

3 On the chalkboard, write some more numbers and have the students predict and prove whether they are odd or even. They may want to draw on paper or work with cubes. Try 20, 43, 55, 32, and so on, as time permits.

THREE CHALLENGE QUESTIONS

4 Ask the students to consider three challenge questions:

- *Which kind of number do you think we would get if we added an even number to an odd number?*
- *What about odd plus odd?*
- *What about even plus even?*

5 Let the students make predictions. Then have them experiment with their cubes or on paper to confirm their theories about each challenge question.

> Even + even numbers will always give an even number. Even + odd numbers will always give an odd number. Odd + odd numbers will always give an even number. Allowing the students to experiment will give them the chance to actually prove it to themselves and really understand it. The mental pictures formed in the students' minds here are important.

Convincing Readers

We explain our procedures and provide examples to convince someone else our theories about odd and even numbers are correct.

USING PROCEDURES AND EXAMPLES

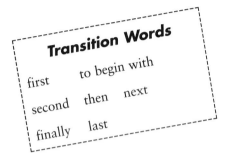

Transition Words

first   to begin with

second   then   next

finally   last

1 *Now your challenge is to write a paragraph to convince a reader that one of your theories is correct. First you will need to explain your procedure.* Ask pairs of students to choose a theory and work together to recall what they did to prove it.

2 *Good procedures follow a logical order. Here are some words to help you sequence your procedures.* Write the transition words on chart paper. Add to the list as students encounter other transition words.

3 *Providing examples is another way to convince someone. Make a list of examples that prove your theory.*

WRITING TO CONVINCE

Paragraph Format

• Topic Sentence:
  Your Theory

• Supporting Sentences:
  Procedure

• Supporting Sentences:
  Examples

• Concluding Sentences:
  Theory Restated

4 Have each student use the procedures and examples they brainstormed with their partners to write their paragraphs. Display the Paragraph Format transparency on the overhead projector and discuss it together. *Use this format to help you organize your theory and proof.* Have students write on one side of their paper only and skip lines; this will simplify the revision process.

> The writing formats throughout *Writing Mathematics* are presented as frames for student writing only—support for students as they develop independence. Although a wonderful modeling technique, formats should never constrain or overpower the students' own thinking or creativity.

REVISING FOR CLARITY

5 Refer students to their editing checklists to help focus their editing efforts. In addition, challenge them to edit for clarity. *Think about how to make your writing clear to someone else. Perhaps illustrations will help to demonstrate your thinking.*

> Throughout *Writing Mathematics*, editing and revising are presented as one step, although they involve two different processes. Revising focuses on the structure and content of the text; editing focuses on mechanics. It is important to limit the focus of a particular revision or editing task.

BELIEVE IT OR NOT

6 Have the students share their paragraphs with someone outside the class. Attach a copy of Dear Reader to each paragraph to help the readers respond.

ASSESSMENT

To assess this writing activity, evaluate how well the students communicate their understanding of odd and even numbers in a convincing paragraph.

- *Did the reader understand the writer's theory and proof?*

- *Does the paragraph include a topic sentence followed by a sequential procedure, examples, and concluding sentences?*

(Classroom Talk)

MAKING OUR WRITING CLEAR

Writers seldom make their writing clear and interesting in their first attempt. Only with experience do students come to view the revision step as an essential part of the writing process. Here are some suggestions for helping students learn to revise.

- Talk regularly about writing as a process of which revision is a natural step.
- Set aside a special time, separate from the initial writing, in which students focus only on revising their text.
- Model the revision process for the students on a regular basis. You will be demonstrating not only revision strategies, but also, the importance of revision.
- Limit the focus of a particular revision task to make it manageable for students.

Convince Me!

MATHEMATICS FOCUS

Discussing Strategies

A network of patterns and relationships can be constructed among the basic arithmetic facts. Unknown sums and differences can be determined by using mental counting strategies.

Students share their thinking and solutions for a range and variety of arithmetic problems, presented one at a time. Students then write in their journals about one other problem.

....

PREPARATION Familiarize yourself with the Guidelines for "Convince Me!" Discussions and the suggested problems. Have journals available.

TIME 4 sessions, then ongoing throughout the year

WRITING FOCUS

Keeping a Journal

The informal writing students do in journals creates opportunities to find out how students feel about themselves and mathematics, and serves as a tool for reflection and self-assessment.

Students extend their writing about "Convince Me!" problems to include writing about their attitudes toward mathematics. A collection of entries becomes a vehicle for an end of the year reflection by each student.

....

PREPARATION Provide a journal for each student and for yourself.

TIME 1 session, then on a weekly basis throughout the year

Discussing Strategies

In "Convince Me!" discussions, we come face to face with our own understandings and misconceptions.

THINKING ON OUR OWN

Problems for "Convince Me!" Discussions

6 + 7	28 + 14	25 − 10
19 + 3	10 + 14	32 − 16
23 + 26	24 + 14	14 − 6
13 + 5	116 + 40	27 − 8
15 + 6	13 − 3	120 − 15

1 For the next several days, familiarize your class with the "Convince Me!" way of thinking about problems. Select problems from the box at left, or others you create, presenting and discussing one at a time. On the chalkboard write a problem. *Think about the answer to this problem.* Follow the Guidelines for "Convince Me!" Discussions, below.

Guidelines for "Convince Me!" Discussions

■ After presenting a problem, allow time for students to think about and solve it. Ask for students' responses. Record the different solutions on the board.

■ Do not indicate the rightness or wrongness of each answer. Be aware of any hints your body language or the inflection of your voice might convey.

■ Encourage a class debate about the correct solution, requesting that students "convince" each other and you of their thinking.

■ Insist that students' explanations rely on number sense, not on following rules.

■ Ask for several different explanations for each problem. Does everyone agree? Can someone tell us a different way to think about the problem?

■ As students explain their thinking, allow them to discover their own errors. Let the final conclusion about which answer is right come from the class, through discourse, not from you.

WRITING OUR STRATEGIES

2 At the end of each math time, write on the chalkboard three or four problems similar to those you've been discussing. *In your journal, write one of these problems and its answer. Write words to tell about your thinking.*

Keeping A Journal

As we write in journals, an extended conversation about our learning becomes part of our experience of mathematics.

WRITING ABOUT THINKING

1 *Your journal will be a diary of your own thinking, a record of your journey in mathematics this year. It will also let me know more about your thinking, and enable me to respond to you individually.*

2 In addition to the "Convince Me!" problems, a question about the students' thinking about their ability to solve problems should be the topic of journal writing once a week or so.

- *What problem were you particularly proud of solving? Tell why.*
- *Have there been problems presented that you have had a difficult time understanding? Explain.*
- *Do you enjoy the "Convince Me!" discussions? Why or why not?*
- *Tell about something you learned from someone else during the "Convince Me!" discussions.*
- *Explain how someone else solved a problem and how you thought about it differently.*
- *Tell about what you are particularly good at in math.*

REVISING TO SHARE

3 Periodically, have students choose one of their journal entries and revise it for someone else to read. *Select an entry that reflects your best thinking or reveals a question that you have.* Refer students to their editing checklists.

4 As students revise their entries, meet with individuals to focus their editing strategies. Suggest one or two proof-reading activities. Refer to Classroom Talk on page 33 for suggestions for writing conferences.

5 Collect students' revised journal entries and pass them out randomly. *Read the journal entry and respond.*

TIME FOR REFLECTION

6 Make a note in your plan book to ask students at the end of the year to select ten journal entries that best illustrate the development of their learning of mathematics. Have students give each entry a title, create a table of contents, and write a brief introduction.

ASSESSMENT

Students' self confidence and disposition toward mathematics influence their success as problem solvers. Use the journals to assess each student's feelings and thinking about mathematics.

- *How does the student view herself as a mathematician?*

- *Is the student able to think about strategies used to solve a problem?*

(Classroom Talk)

ENCOURAGING JOURNAL CONVERSATIONS

Journals are a wonderful vehicle for extended, individual conversations with students. To encourage journal writing, follow these guidelines:

- Keep your own journal. Occasionally share your journal entries with your students.
- Allow students some privacy in their journals. Have some way, such as folded page corners, to indicate pages the student wishes you to read. Let students know ahead of time if certain entries will be read.
- Encourage students to write without concern for mechanics. Assure them you will not be looking at spelling, grammar, or punctuation.
- When responding, show your interest by acknowledging students' feelings, praising their thinking, sharing your ideas, or prompting students to clarify or extend their thinking.
- Don't keep the students' journals for more than twenty-four hours. Do respond in writing to every journal entry you read. Some responses may be very short–simple statements of agreement or short prompts.

The Giant Chart

MATHEMATICS FOCUS

Organizing Arrays

Arrays can be used to model combining situations. Multiplication equations are number sentences that can be used to record problems involving equal groups.

Students build rectangular models of multiplication facts. They describe the rectangles using "rows of" language, write multiplication equations, and organize the facts on a giant multiplication chart.

....

MATERIALS

❑ 1-cm grid paper (page 44)

❑ full sheets of paper

❑ chart paper

❑ scissors

❑ 1 paper bag

For each pair

❑ 100 Rainbow Cubes in one color

TIME 5 sessions

WRITING FOCUS

Addressing an Audience

A writer can make use of differences in style, tone, and word choice to address specific audiences, such as a gremlin and a governor. Using proper letter form is important.

Students think about the attributes of each of their intended audiences, then write letters to both. They mail their letters to the real intended audiences, and consider any responses they receive.

....

MATERIALS

❑ writing paper

PREPARATION Before modeling the editing process, ask two students to volunteer their letters. Make transparencies of the letters.

TIME 2-3 sessions

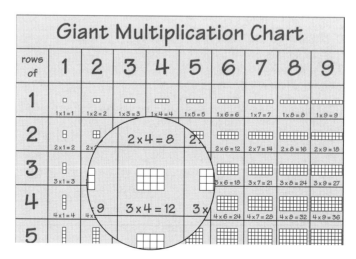

To make the chart, cut a square of colored butcher paper $5\frac{1}{2}'$ on a side. Draw a grid of 6" squares, ten across and ten down. Label the top and leftmost rows with the numbers 1 to 9. Prepare a few grid-paper rectangles, place them on the chart, and write equations below them.

Organizing Arrays

We get to know the patterns that exist on our chart. Then the gremlin can't trick us!

FILLING IN THE CHART

2 x 1 = 2   2 x 5 = 10

3 x 2 = 6   3 x 3 = 9   3 x 4 = 12

4 x 1 = 4   4 x 2 = 8   4 x 3 = 12

8 x 1 = 8

REPAIRING THE CHART

1 Introduce the Giant Multiplication Chart and ask what students notice about it. After discussing their observations about the rectangles and equations, have students use their cubes to make more rectangles and record them with grid paper. Have pairs continue to work, saving their grid-paper recordings until the class meets each day.

2 Midway through math time, gather near the chart. *See if you can figure out where your rectangles go.* Have students take turns placing a rectangle on the chart and writing the equation. (Put the rectangles on the chart in such a way that they can be removed later.)

3 At the end of math each day, discuss the patterns that are emerging and record on chart paper the students' observations. As you point to an empty space on the chart, ask students to predict what equation will go there and tell how they know.

4 The day after the chart is completed, secretly remove and place in a bag one rectangle for each student. As class begins, explain that a sneaky gremlin has stolen some of their rectangles, but that you found a bag of them that he must have dropped.

5 Pass out one rectangle from the bag to each student. *Figure out where your rectangle belongs and write a letter to the gremlin telling him how you know where the rectangle belongs on the chart.*

Using "rows of" language will help students determine the equation for and placement of each rectangle. The chart reads from left to right, with the number of rows listed down the left edge and the number in each row across the top. Thus, the rectangle for the equation 3 x 4 = 12 (3 rows of 4) is oriented differently than the rectangle for the equation 4 x 3 = 12 (4 rows of 3). It is important that the students orient their grid-paper rectangles correctly on the chart so that patterns can begin to emerge as the chart fills.

Addressing an Audience

We learn to use changes in style, tone, and word choice to get our point across.

TALKING ABOUT AUDIENCE

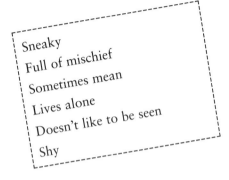

Sneaky
Full of mischief
Sometimes mean
Lives alone
Doesn't like to be seen
Shy

1 *Since the receiver of the letter is the gremlin, let's think about what we know about the gremlin.* Discuss how the attributes of gremlins might influence the students' style of writing.

2 Ask the students to think about what would be different if they were writing to the governor of your state.

3 *We want to get across the idea that we don't want our rectangles disturbed again. With your partner, write a sentence that conveys that idea to a gremlin and another sentence that conveys that idea to our governor.* Discuss differences in style, tone, and word choice.

WRITING LETTERS

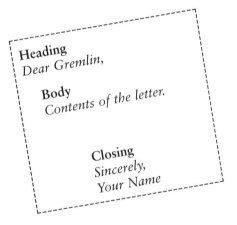

Heading
Dear Gremlin,

Body
Contents of the letter.

Closing
Sincerely,
Your Name

4 Before the students begin their letters, review proper letter writing form. *As you write, picture in your mind the gremlin receiving your letter and reading it.*

5 When the students have finished their letters to the gremlin, challenge them to write another letter to a real audience telling about the multiplication chart and how they know where each rectangle belongs.

6 *Before you begin the letter, think about how this letter will be different because of your new audience.* Have students write who their new audience is, list two things they will do differently because of their new audience, then write their letters.

MODELING THE EDITING PROCESS

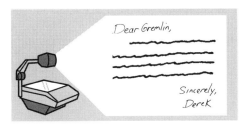

Dear Gremlin,

Sincerely,
Derek

7 Display the letters you have prepared on transparencies and ask the students who wrote them to read them aloud. Ask the class to comment on the content and mechanics of each letter. Note the class's suggestions right on the transparency.

- *What has the author of the letter done well?*
- *Is there something that needs to be changed?*
- *Is there anything that is unclear? How would you make it more clear?*

IN FAVOR OF A REPLY

8 Encourage the students to mail their letters. Review the proper format for addressing envelopes. Plan to share any replies received. Discuss the tone of the received letter.

ASSESSMENT

For this writing activity, it is important not to take the role of evaluator; otherwise, students, consciously or unconsciously, see you as the audience. Evaluate how well the students communicate their understanding of multiplication in their letters addressing different audiences.

- *Does the student accomplish her two goals in changing the tone of the second letter?*
- *Does the student use the proper letter writing format?*

(Classroom Talk)

ORAL LANGUAGE AND WRITING

Oral language is the foundation of writing. The discussions which take place prior to writing focus students' thinking about the writing task, draw upon their prior knowledge, build vocabulary, and present new thoughts and concepts. Every student leaves the discussions with something to say, a result that nurtures self-esteem.

These oral language experiences prior to writing take many forms, including: brainstorming, role playing, sharing literature, holding discussions in large or small groups, and interviewing peers.

The teacher's role in facilitating oral language experiences changes from the traditional one of asking questions for which she already knows the answers, waiting for specific responses, and imposing the definitive "right/wrong" judgment, to the challenge of posing open-ended questions that extend students' thinking. In this new role, the teacher encourages students to think out loud, explore alternative strategies, and entertain their classmates' points of view.

Crazy Creatures

MATHEMATICS FOCUS

Creating Attribute Sets

By manipulating the various values within a defined set of attributes, a collection of all the unique combinations possible can be created. Combination problems have a finite solution set.

Students approach a big combination problem by thinking about a smaller version of it. They then work with partners to produce their own complete set of Creature Cards, figuring out all the combinations of the given attributes.

....

MATERIALS

For each pair

❏ 40 note cards (3" x 5") unlined

❏ crayons or colored pencils

❏ 1 medium plastic bag

❏ full sheets of paper

PREPARATION To begin, have an overhead projector and a blank transparency ready.

TIME 3-4 sessions

WRITING FOCUS

Planning a Project

Writing an organized plan is an effective way to approach, carry out, and create a record of the Crazy Creatures project. Plans are guides which can be revised.

Students brainstorm things to think about as they write plans. Students' written plans guide their work on the project. They evaluate their plans daily, talking and comparing plans with classmates.

....

MATERIALS

❏ chart paper

❏ writing paper

TIME concurrent sessions

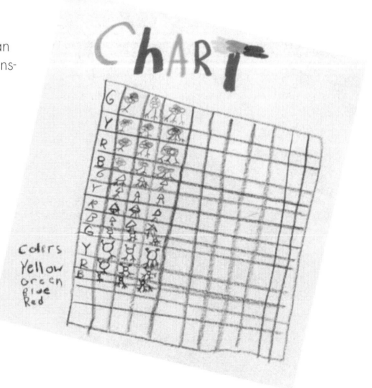

Creating Attribute Sets

The process of creating our sets challenges us to be logical and organized.

DRAWING BOOLEAN CREATURES

1 *I'd like you to meet the three different types of creatures on the planet Boole: Googlies, Squiggles, and Tri-guys.* Draw the three body types on the overhead. Explain that all three types can be either red or blue.

2 Have the students work with partners to discover how many different Boolean creatures there can be.

3 When the students have found all the possible combinations (there are 6), get together and let students describe them. Draw each at the overhead, so students can keep track. Explain that a set that shows all the different combinations you can make with certain characteristics is called an attribute set.

MAKING A LARGER SET

4 *I was wondering what would happen if we said that these creatures could come in 4 colors and have 1, 2, or 3 legs?*

5 Provide each pair with forty note cards and challenge them to create a complete set of the new Boolean creatures. Write the attributes on the chalkboard for the students to refer to as they work. (Have students save their sets in plastic bags.)

6 *Creating Creature Cards is a big project. Before any big problem-solving challenge, thinking about and writing out a plan is a good idea.* Refer to Planning a Project (pages 20-21).

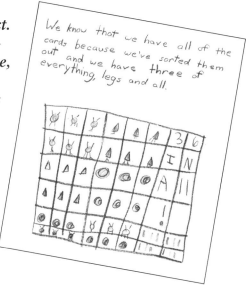

Planning a Project

As we create and revise our plans, we get new ideas by talking to each other.

DEVISING A PLAN

1 As a class, brainstorm a list of things to think about as the students write their plans. Write the responses on chart paper.

2 Challenge students to write their plans. As they work, pose questions to encourage them to address the things listed on the chart. Once they have written their plan, students can begin to work on their Creature Cards.

EVALUATING THE PLAN

3 As students work on their sets of Creature Cards, remind them to think about their plans. Mention any steps you see the pairs taking and ask, *Did you write that into your plan?*

Things to Think About When Making a Plan

- What is our job?
- What do we need to do it?
- What steps do we take?
- How will we know we are done?

4 At the end of math time each day, allow time for the students to evaluate their plans and revise as necessary. Encourage them to share their plans with other students.

- *Did you follow your plan? Explain.*
- *Did you do anything that was not on your plan? Explain.*
- *Did you get any ideas from others that you might try in your plan?*
- *Do you need to change your plan so you are more productive tomorrow? Explain.*

Making plans requires critical thinking and is a skill that increases with time and practice. Students will approach this task at many different levels. Encourage students to view their plans as guides to be revised as necessary.

REVISING THE PLAN

5 The revision stage of writing plans is ongoing. Students modify, add, and delete steps as they work each day. On the final day, challenge the students to rewrite their plans as an accurate record of their procedures.

MORE THAN ONE WAY TO...

6 Have students share their finished plans with another pair. Then come together as a class and talk about the effectiveness of the different plans.

- *How is your plan similar to the other pair's plan? How is it different?*
- *Are the plans clear?*
- *Could you follow the other plan to complete the task? Explain.*

ASSESSMENT

To assess this writing activity, evaluate how well the students communicate their understanding of attribute sets in their finished plans.

- *Is the student's plan clear and complete?*
- *Did the student revise the plan to make it more complete and clear?*

(Classroom Talk)

ENCOURAGING THE EXCHANGE OF IDEAS

Classroom discussions in which students have opportunities to share their ideas and listen to the views of their peers make students active participants in their own learning and promote real understandings of mathematics. As part of the discourse in your classroom, expect students to pose questions, consider the viewpoints of others, and explain their thinking.

In many classrooms, students have come to rely on the teachers as the sole judges of "right" and "wrong." Consequently, many students hold back responses unless they are reasonably sure they have the right answer, then look to the teacher for validation. By directing students to their peers for validation or for other viewpoints, you will change this communication pattern.

- *Sally, what do you think about Philip and Gina's plan?*
- *Amy and Robbie, how is your plan like Joey and Marissa's plan? How is it different?*
- *Will anyone use part of this plan in your own plan? Explain.*

As students work in pairs and small groups, encourage productive conversation. Joining a small group as a participant will allow you to model language and interactions for your students.

Fraction Images

MATHEMATICS FOCUS

Finding Fractions

When a whole region is divided into equivalent parts, each part can be named as a fraction of the whole. The same fractional numeral can describe regions that look quite different. For any fractional numeral, there are many other equivalent fractional numerals that describe the quantity.

Students explore the set of plastic fraction pieces and practice writing the fraction symbol. They then use the fraction pieces to find equivalent fractions, make recordings, and practice the language of fractions.

....

MATERIALS

For each pair
❑ Fraction Circles PLUS™
(one set of 51 pieces)
❑ writing paper
❑ colored markers or crayons

PREPARATION Set up overhead projector and Fraction Squares PLUS™.

TIME 2 sessions

WRITING FOCUS

Using Mathematical Symbols

Mathematicians use many symbols as shorthand for conveying mathematical ideas. Fraction notation is one form of shorthand. Equations can communicate meaning.

Students list mathematical symbols they are familiar with, then focus on fractional notation. They illustrate fraction equivalencies by making drawings, using fraction notation, and writing stories.

....

MATERIALS
❑ chart paper
❑ writing paper
❑ colored markers or crayons

PREPARATION Have fraction pieces from the math sessions available.

TIME 2 sessions

And then we'll see how many equal parts are in each circle.

Let's put together circles with the same color pieces.

Finding Fractions

Our work leaves us with multiple mental images of fractions.

PLAYING WHAT'S MY RULE?

1 Play *What's My Rule?* with your class. On the chalkboard draw shapes divided into halves in the *In* section, and shapes divided into parts that are not halves in the *Out* section. **On your paper draw a shape and divide it into parts.** Have several students add their shapes to the appropriate section on the board. Ask a volunteer to verbalize the rule. Repeat the game for rules that involve each of the other fractions in the set as the *In* shape.

2 On the overhead projector, use Fraction Squares to display the whole square and two halves. Indicate one half and write the symbol. **This is the way the fraction one half is written. To read this fraction we can say, one part out of two equal parts.** Display other fractions in this way (including fractions such as two thirds and three fifths), and ask students to write the symbols. Continue until writing the fraction symbol seems easy.

FINDING EQUIVALENT FRACTIONS

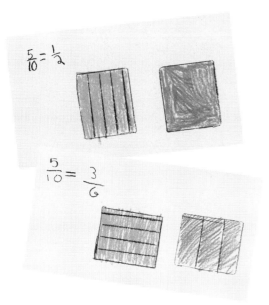

3 Tell the pairs to search for pieces that, when combined, are equivalent to the one-third piece in their set. **Who can tell me a combination of fraction pieces that exactly cover the one-third piece?** Restate the students' responses as, for example:

Two sixths equals one third.
One sixth and two twelfths is equivalent to one third.

4 Next tell the pairs to find their tenths pieces and show five tenths. **Now find other fraction pieces that are equivalent to five tenths.** Have students record what they find using pictures and symbols.

5 Have the students share their recordings with the class. Practice the language of fractions, such as:

Five tenths is equivalent to one half.
Five tenths is equal to one fourth plus two eighths.
Ask, **Can anyone think of another fraction equivalent to five tenths that no one recorded?**

Using Mathematical Symbols

We "break the code" of other students' stories, using our fraction notation know-how.

EXPLORING SYMBOLS

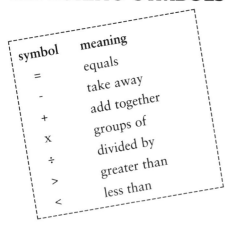

symbol	meaning
=	equals
-	take away
+	add together
x	groups of
÷	divided by
>	greater than
<	less than

1 *Mathematicians use many symbols as shorthand for conveying mathematical ideas.* Draw an equals sign on the chalkboard. *For example, what does this symbol mean?*

2 *What other mathematical symbols do you know?* Have students work in groups to create lists of mathematical symbols. Then record their responses on chart paper and discuss the meaning of each symbol.

3 If no one brought up fraction notation as mathematical shorthand introduce it yourself. *What about $\frac{3}{4}$?* Review the parts of a fractional numeral.

USING SYMBOLS

4 *Today we are going to focus on using fraction shorthand to communicate meaning.* Have pairs of students draw five different pictures illustrating fraction equivalencies. Then have them write the shorthand fraction equation that describes each picture.

EDITING FOR ACCURACY

5 Explain to the students that they will be trading their fraction pictures and equations with another pair. *Be sure to check your work for accuracy.*

BREAKING THE CODE

6 Have pairs trade fraction pictures and equations. *Write a complete story situation describing the fraction equation and picture you've been given.*

$$\frac{1}{2} = \frac{3}{6}$$

Mary, Sue and Kelly had a Pizza Party. Each girl had one piece of Pizza, and half the Pizza was Left. How much of the Pizza did each girl eat?

7 Allow time for pairs to share their favorite story situation. You may want to bind these in a book or post them on a bulletin board.

ASSESSMENT

To assess this activity, evaluate how well students communicate their understanding of equivalent fractions in their illustrated story situations.

- *Are the fraction equivalencies and their illustrations accurate?*

- *Has the student represented the fraction equivalencies in an interesting story situation?*

(Classroom Talk)

DEVELOPING MATHEMATICAL VOCABULARY

Throughout mathematics, specialized vocabulary is necessary for concise and effective communication. Mathematical vocabulary includes special terms, diagrams, graphs, sketches, and symbols. To promote vocabulary development, keep the following suggestions in mind.

- Introduce and use all mathematical vocabulary as tools for talking about ideas.

- Show appreciation for students' efforts to use new words and symbols. Address students' errors in usage informally as they work and talk.

- Challenge students to listen as words or symbols are used during activities. Then have the students discuss their meanings. If you write definitions on the board, use the students' language as much as possible.

Measuring Around

MATHEMATICS FOCUS

Exploring Perimeter

All measurements are approximations. The selection of a measuring tool for a task depends on the exactness of the measurement needed. The perimeter of an object or shape is the measure around its edges.

Students make their own inch rulers and tape measures, use them to find the perimeter of classroom objects, and make perimeter books that show the objects measured and their dimensions.

....

MATERIALS

For each student
❑ 1 strip of tag board, 12″ x 2″
❑ 1 Rainbow Tile
For each pair
❑ 15$\frac{1}{2}$′ strip of adding machine tape
❑ 1 cardboard tube
❑ 1 paper clip
❑ 26 half-sheets of paper

PREPARATION Make a sample 12-inch ruler and 15-foot tape measure from the materials students will use. Have a small box for demonstrating measuring. Post a piece of butcher paper with the headings: 1 to 6″, 7 to 11″, 1 to 6′, 7 to 15′.

TIME 4 sessions

WRITING FOCUS

Comparing Tools

Comparisons of and contrasts between our measurement tools can be written about in an organized paragraph, using words that signal similarities and differences.

Students organize their ideas about rulers and tape measures using a Venn diagram. Paragraphs comparing and contrasting the two tools are written and revised, in preparation for a class debate.

....

MATERIALS

❑ writing paper

PREPARATION   Post a piece of butcher paper for the Venn diagram recording.

TIME   2-3 sessions

Exploring Perimeter

Thinking about approximations is what this activity is all about.

MAKING TOOLS

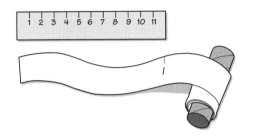

1. *What do you think the perimeter, the measure all the way around, of our door might be? How could we find out?* Take responses. *Let's make tools to find the perimeter of objects in the room.*

2. Point out that your sample ruler is 12 inches long—the same as 1 foot. Help students see that your tape is 15 feet long. Distribute tiles and tag board. *Each edge of a tile is the same as 1 inch. Can you make a 12-inch ruler using the tile and tag board?*

3. After making rulers, students should find a partner, then pick up adding machine tape and a tube. *Now make a measuring tape that is 15 feet long. Remember, your 12-inch ruler is 1 foot long.*

HUNTING AROUND

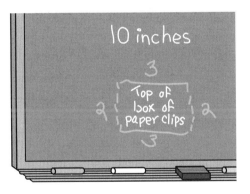

4. When the rulers and tapes are made, have two students demonstrate for the class how to measure the distance around one face of a small box. Make a record on the chalkboard as shown. Ask another pair to find the perimeter of a door.

5. Have pairs of students create 26-page perimeter books, labeling a page 1 inch, the next 2 inches, and so on up to 11 inches, then a page for 1 foot, 2 feet, and on up to 15 feet.

6. *To hunt perimeters, measure an object and record its perimeter on the page that's <u>closest</u> to its measurement. Make a record like the one on the chalkboard.*

7. Toward the end of math time each day, gather students together near the butcher paper. Under the appropriate headings, enter the names of objects the students found. *Did you use a ruler or a tape?*

Comparing Tools

We present convincing statements comparing the usefulness of rulers and measuring tapes.

THINKING ABOUT TOOLS

1 *We've been using our rulers and measuring tapes to measure lots of different things. Let's think about how rulers and measuring tapes are alike and how they are different and display our findings on a Venn diagram.*

2 Draw two intersecting circles on the butcher paper you've posted. Label the circles *Rulers* and *Measuring Tapes*. As students suggest things about rulers and measuring tapes, place their responses in the appropriate places on the Venn diagram.

WRITING TO COMPARE

3 *When writing to compare and contrast, it can be helpful to use signal words.* Write the words at left on the board. Ask students to use the words in sentences describing rulers and measuring tapes.

4 Have the students use the information on the Venn diagram to write a paragraph comparing and contrasting rulers and measuring tapes. *Remember that your paragraph should have a topic sentence, three or four supporting sentences, and a concluding sentence.*

COMPARING WORDS

- both
- alike
- also
- same as
- like, similar

CONTRASTING WORDS

- but
- different
- in contrast
- however
- on the other hand

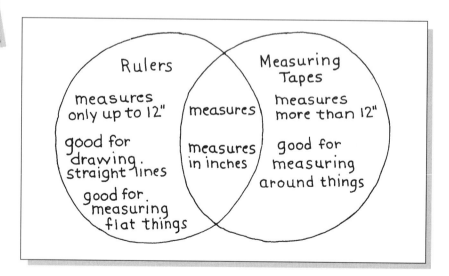

Rulers
- measures only up to 12"
- good for drawing straight lines
- good for measuring flat things

measures
measures in inches

Measuring Tapes
- measures more than 12"
- good for measuring around things

REVISING WITH EDITING PARTNERS

5 Have students choose a partner they would like to have edit their writing. *Tell your partner three things to look for in your writing.*

6 When the partners finish reading, have them meet with the writers and make suggestions. Provide time for the writers to revise their paragraphs.

THE GREAT DEBATE

7 *The leader of the world has decided that only one measuring tool can exist, either a ruler or a measuring tape.* Divide the class into two groups, one supporting rulers, and the other, measuring tapes. *Your group's job is to convince this leader that your measuring tool should be chosen. Together, make up a list of reasons your tool is the better one.*

8 When the groups are finished, have them share their lists. *Based on the evidence presented here, which measuring tool should the leader choose?*

ASSESSMENT

To assess this writing activity, evaluate how well students communicate their understanding of measurement in their paragraphs and presentations comparing and contrasting measuring tools.

- *Does the student include at least one sentence to compare and one to contrast in a well organized paragraph?*

- *Are the student's comparisons well thought out?*

(Classroom Talk)

USING DISCOURSE TO PROMOTE THINKING

Students' thinking is revealed as they verbalize ideas. As students exchange ideas, they begin to engage in processes of metacognition– monitoring, regulating, and evaluating. Participation in groups and in whole class discussions helps students generate new ideas and transfer what is learned to new situations with greater success.

In this lesson, the class brainstorms ways rulers and measuring tapes are alike and different, and the teacher uses a Venn diagram to help them organize their ideas. The resulting recording is much richer than would be lists generated by students individually.

Pentomino Search

MATHEMATICS FOCUS

Constructing Shapes

Shapes can be used in combination to make other shapes. An understanding of rotation can be developed through explorations using familiar objects.

Students discern the rules for building pentominoes, then pairs use Pattern Block squares and visual thinking to find the twelve possible arrangements. Pairs record each shape on grid paper to make their own sets of pentominoes.

. . . .

MATERIALS

　　For each pair

❑　5 orange Rainbow Tiles

❑　1-inch grid paper (page 45)

PREPARATION　To begin, have ready an overhead projector and Rainbow Tiles (5 orange).

TIME　1 session

WRITING FOCUS

Giving Directions

Manipulating real objects and keeping track of steps as they happen make writing directions for creating pentominoes easier. Using only words, without diagrams, is a challenge.

Students give and receive verbal directions, then write directions for making all twelve pentominoes. To identify needed revisions, pairs try to follow their own directions and exchange directions with another pair.

. . . .

MATERIALS

　　For each pair

❑　a file folder and their complete set of pentominoes

❑　full sheets of paper

PREPARATION　Make a copy for each student of Pentomino Puzzles (page 46).

TIME　2-3 sessions

Constructing Shapes

We explore pentominoes. How many arrangements can we find?

WHAT ARE THE RULES?

1 *Today we'll be building a special group of shapes called pentominoes.* Use Rainbow Tiles to show some valid and invalid examples of pentomino shapes on the overhead projector. *What do you think the rules for building pentominoes are?*

FINDING ALL TWELVE

These are pentominoes

These are not pentominoes

2 *There are 12 possible ways to arrange your squares into pentominoes. Work with your partner. Try to find all 12 pentominoes shapes. Record each pentomino shape you find on your grid paper.* Make sure the students understand that each shape must be different. If a shape can be flipped or turned to make another shape, it is not different.

> Make sure that the following pentominoes "rules" have been mentioned and are clear to the students: All pentominoes are made from 5 squares. Pentominoes are flat. Whole sides of squares must touch.

3 At the end of math time, get together as a class to compare pentomino shapes. As an extra challenge, students can try to find which shapes fold into boxes without tops.

The 12 Pentominoes

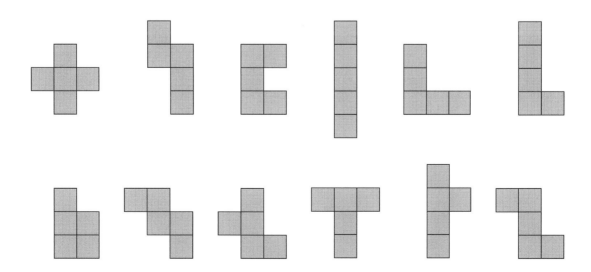

Giving Directions

We find out whether writing directions is as easy as we thought.

FOLLOWING ORAL DIRECTIONS

1 *Pentominoes are great for creating puzzles and designs.* Provide each student with a copy of the Pentomino Puzzles. Encourage students to try both puzzles, then experiment with their pentominoes to make their own designs.

2 Have students select one of their designs to play the Barrier Game. Explain the game to the class.

3 After all the students have had an opportunity to give directions, talk about their experiences.

- *What did you learn by giving directions? by receiving?*
- *Was it easier to give or receive directions? Why?*
- *Were there directions you gave that the receiver took in a different way? Explain.*

WRITING DIRECTIONS

4 *Now, instead of giving directions orally, your challenge is to write the directions for making your design.* Encourage the students to think about what they did to build their design and the oral directions they gave during the Barrier Game.

5 Have students include in their directions a short introduction and step-by-step directions. Challenge the students to use only words, no diagrams.

Rules for The Barrier Game

1. Two players need a file folder and their own set of pentomino shapes.
2. The players sit facing one another with the file folder acting as a wall between them.
3. One player makes a pentomino design. The other, who cannot see the design, re-creates the design from verbal instructions given by the creator.
4. When the players feel the design has been re-created, they lift the wall and compare designs.
5. Players then reverse roles and play the game a second time.

REVISING DIRECTIONS **6** After putting their writing away for at least a day, have students return to their directions. *Read through your directions. Do only what they say. Are your directions clear?* As the students work independently, meet briefly for a writing conference with individual students to help focus their revising and editing strategies.

STEP BY STEP **7** Have pairs exchange directions with another pair. *Follow the directions exactly. Are you able to make the pentomino design? What suggestions do you have for making the directions more clear?*

ASSESSMENT Interview pairs as they work with their own and another pair's directions. Evaluate their ability to sequence steps, and to revise their work. Ask:

- *Are you able to follow the directions to complete the task? Why or why not?*

- *How could the directions be more clear?*

(Classroom Talk)

THE WRITING CONFERENCE

Writing conferences are opportunities for one-to-one communication between teacher and student. During conferences, keep the following practices in mind.

- Show an interest in what the student has to say, both orally and in writing.
- Take note of the student's language strengths and weaknesses.
- Leave the pencil in the student's hand.
- Most importantly, be positive.
- Instead of telling a student how to revise or edit their writing, use questions like the following to draw the need for revisions from the student.
  - *What do you like best about what you've written? Why?*
  - *Is there a part that you aren't happy with? Why?*
  - *I don't follow this part. Can you tell me more?*
  - *The words on the page don't tell me that. Can you include that idea in your writing?*
  - *What's the most important thing you are saying in this piece?*

Animal Research

MATHEMATICS FOCUS

Displaying Data

Mathematics is used in many ways in the world around us. Problem solving can be especially meaningful when applied to real-world settings.

Students research animals, collecting numerical data. This information is displayed in a large class database, then students estimate figures to fill in any empty cells.

....

MATERIALS

❑ Animals of the Zoo cards

❑ push pins

❑ inch rulers and foot measuring tapes

PREPARATION   Gather resource books.

TIME   3 sessions

WRITING FOCUS

Reporting On Animals

Formats for note taking and structuring paragraphs are effective ways to collect and organize information about animals for a report.

Students brainstorm topics to research, then learn a format for organizing their notes. They write and edit reports which are shared and displayed.

....

MATERIALS

❑ writing paper

❑ supplies for report covers

PREPARATION   Resource books should be available. Make a copy for each student of Editing Checklist (page 48).

TIME   4 sessions

Animal Data Table

Animal	Weight at Birth	Adult Weight	Height	Length	Number of Babies	Grou Size
lion	3 or 4 lbs				1 to 6	
heron	72 kg		4 ft.			8 – 5
brown bear			9 ft.			8 to 5
polar bear				5-12 ft		
vulture	12 to 13 lbs				1	7
red deer		30 to 50 lbs				
iguana				12 inches		
toucan						

Use yarn lengths to set up the grid for your Animal Data Table. Cut full sheets of paper into quarters widthwise for the strips. Put the column headings up. Row headings will be added by the students.

Displaying Data

Our research is focused on numbers, as we gather data to compare animals to each other.

PLANNING THE DISPLAYS

TRACKING DOWN THE FACTS

Can we use information that we have to make educated guesses about the missing information?

I bet a lion is about the same as a tiger. We know how tall a tiger is —about 3 feet.

Right. So a lion is about 3 feet tall, too.

What does everyone else think?

1 *We're going to pretend to be animal researchers this week.* Have each pair draw a card from the bag of Animal of the Zoo cards and think of several clues they could use to describe the animal. Go around the class letting each pair give two or three clues about their animal.

2 Point out the grid on the bulletin board. *Our challenge is to complete this table of animal information. Your job is to research your Zoo card animal and fill in as many cells as you can with data for your animal.* Have each pair write the name of their animal on a strip and pin it in the first column of the chart to form row headings.

3 Next, point out the column headings on the table. *As you read about your animals, keep your eyes open for this information. Add it to our data table as you find it.* (Have strips and push pins available near the table.)

4 For the next few days, students will need to share the Animals of the Zoo cards and the resource books. Try to keep the class focused on inches and feet, instead of metric measurements.

5 At the end of math time each day, bring the class together to share ideas.

- *What's the most interesting thing you've learned so far?*
- *How did you know where to place information in the table?*

6 When students have added all of their data to the table, suggest they use logical thinking to make educated guesses about the missing information, then fill in the empty cells.

Reporting On Animals

Now we organize our animal data into report form and learn different aspects of the editing process.

GATHERING INFORMATION

1 Explain to the students that they will each write a report about their favorite animal. *Take five minutes and write all you know about your animal.* Have students share what they have written with a partner.

2 *Now take a few minutes to write down things you would like to learn about your animal.* For this report, have students choose four questions to research.

3 Demonstrate how to fold a paper into fourths and head each section for note taking. *As you find information that answers your questions, jot a few words in the appropriate box to help you remember it.*

> While students are engaged in research, encourage them to use the library and librarian's help to search for specific information. You may want to have a mini-lesson on using the index and table of contents to help locate specific information in a book.

WRITING THE REPORT

Report Format

- **Paragraph One:** general information about the animal

- **Paragraphs Two-Five:** specific information about one of the questions

- **Paragraph Six:** general summary information

4 *Once you have found the information that answers your questions, organize each question and the information into a paragraph with three or four sentences.* Explain that the first paragraph of the report should provide general information about the animal, while the following three or four paragraphs should relate information pertaining to the questions the student had.

> Students will require varying amounts of time to gather information and write their reports. Expect that some children will finish in one or two days, while others will take several days.

EDITING TO DISPLAY	**5**	Schedule three mini-lessons to focus on aspects of the editing process. Have students use the appropriate section of the Editing Checklist for each.
FOR YOUR INFORMATION	**6**	Invite students to make decorative covers for their reports. Display the reports on a bulletin board or in the classroom or school library. Include in the reports a page at the end for comments from readers.
ASSESSMENT		To assess this writing activity, evaluate how well students communicate their interpretation of data in a report.

- *Did the student effectively formulate questions and locate information?*
- *Is the report well organized?*

───────────────(Classroom Talk)───────────────

TALKING ABOUT REPORTS

As students work through the steps of report writing, provide ample time for them to talk about what they are learning. These opportunities for productive talk have two goals: that students internalize the information they gather, and that they trust they have something to say. Having this foundation will help students write their reports using their own voice, rather than copying from sources. Here are some recommended activities.

- Begin sessions with five minutes of free writing in which students write without notes "to get to know what they know."
- Alternately, begin sessions by having students write for five minutes, using their notes to formulate complete sentences.
- Start or end sessions with peer interviews, in which students ask each other questions about their topics and use what they remember and their notes to respond.
- End sessions with a class discussion about problems students are encountering. Have students offer suggestions or share information to help others solve their problems.
- Have peers conference about revising and editing.

Tally Ho!

MATHEMATICS FOCUS

Exploring Probability

Playing games and recording results can help in determining the probability that a particular event will occur.

Students play a variation of the game Tic-Tac-Toe, using a numbered game board and dice. They determine the probability of rolling the possible sums, then design a game board to increase their chances of winning.

....

MATERIALS

For each pair

❑ 2 Numeral Dice

❑ 18 Rainbow Cubes of any color

❑ paper for game boards

TIME   1-2 sessions

WRITING FOCUS

Explaining Our Chances

There are many words that describe the chance of an event occurring. Using those words in an organized paragraph is an effective way to explain our thinking about probability.

Students brainstorm a list of words that describe probabilities and explore their meaning as they discuss and write about the probability of winning a Tic-Tac-Toe game using a chosen game board.

....

MATERIALS

For each pair

❑ two numeral dice

❑ 18 Rainbow Cubes of any color

❑ writing paper

❑ chart paper

PREPARATION   Make a copy for each student of Game Boards (page 49) and a transparency of Editing Experts (page 50).

TIME   2 sessions

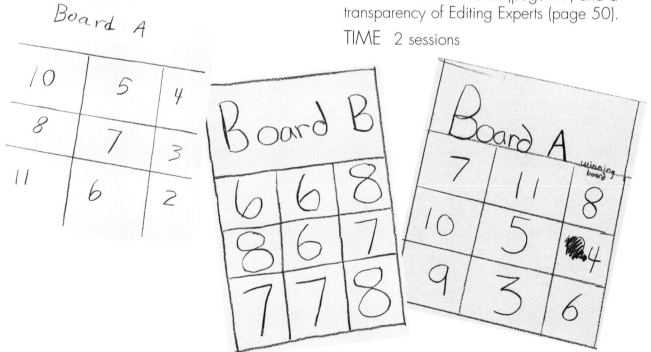

Exploring Probability

We play using several game boards and discover that our results may be quite different.

LEARNING TO PLAY

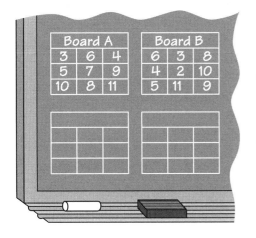

Board A			Board B		
3	6	4	6	3	8
5	7	9	4	2	10
10	8	11	5	11	9

1 *Today we're going to play a new version of Tic-Tac-Toe.* On the chalkboard, draw game boards A and B and the two blank boards, as shown at left. Have pairs make these four boards.

2 Choose a pair of students to roll the dice as you demonstrate how to play the game. On the chalkboard, keep a tally of the number of times each sum is rolled.

3 Have pairs play the game twice, keeping a tally like the one on the chalkboard and switching boards with each other after the first game. Point out that the tally of numbers rolled will help students think about how to make a new game board to their advantage.

DESIGNING TO WIN

4 After pairs have played twice, ask them to look at their tallies.

- *Which sums did you roll most often? What did this have to do with your chances of winning?*
- *Which board gave you the best chance of winning? Why?*

5 *Use the information from your tallies to design a board you think has a good chance of winning. You can use any numbers in any square. You can repeat numbers.* Have each player fill in a blank board, then play the game with a partner.

6 At the end of math time, discuss the pairs' game boards.

- *What strategies did you use to make your own game board?*
- *How well did your strategies work?*
- *Would you make a different game board next time? How?*

It's likely a student will raise the valid point that the board a player plays against is a variable effecting the chances of winning. Listen and observe as students discuss this idea.

Explaining Our Chances

We put forth an explanation of one board's chance of being a winner, then see if the board performs as expected.

EXPLORING WORDS

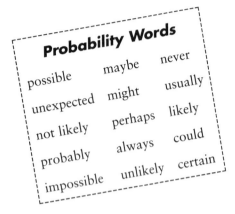

1 *Every day we use words that describe probabilities to talk about the chance of something occurring. For example, how would you describe your chances of getting to have ice cream for dinner? What about your chances of having spaghetti for dinner?* Write the students' responses on chart paper. Ask students to brainstorm a list of words that describe probabilities.

2 On the chalkboard, show students one of the three boards shown below. ***Based on your experience, how would you describe your chances of winning using this board?*** Write the students' responses under the board. Repeat with the other two game boards.

WRITING TO EXPLAIN

3 Distribute copies of the Game Boards. Have students choose a game board and write a paragraph using probability words to explain the chances of winning Tic-Tac-Toe using that board.

4 As always, students' paragraphs should include a topic sentence, three or four supporting sentences, and a concluding sentence. *Your supporting sentences should offer reasons this board has the chances you describe, based on what you know about probability.*

Board A		
13	1	26
32	26	19
30	14	17

Board B		
4	11	3
5	7	9
8	10	6

Board C		
8	7	6
7	7	7
6	7	8

REVISING AND TESTING

I thought my board would win every time, but it's about even with my partner's.

5 Tell students that for the revision process they will each be an expert on one form of editing. Display Editing Experts on the overhead projector. Talk about the roles and the types of questions the experts should ask themselves as they edit a paragraph.

6 Organize students into groups of four and assign each group member an editing task. Each expert will read the four paragraphs written by the members of the group, focusing on one area of expertise, and make revision suggestions for each piece in writing. Once the writers have received their suggestions from the experts, provide time for them to make revisions.

AND THE WINNER IS...

7 Have students make a copy of the game board they wrote about and play a couple of Tic-Tac-Toe games with a partner. Together, discuss the results. *Were the results what you expected?*

ASSESSMENT

To assess this writing activity, evaluate how well students communicate their understanding of probability in a paragraph explaining the chances of winning with a chosen game board.

- *Does the student use mathematical reasoning to support his explanation?*
- *Is the paragraph well organized?*

(Classroom Talk)

THE ROLE OF SILENCE IN DISCOURSE

The role silence plays in discourse cannot be overemphasized. Immediately calling on the first two or three students who raise their hands when a question is posed sends a number of messages: that getting an answer quickly is preferable to puzzling and persevering; that "the one answer," rather than the process of considering many points of view, is the goal; and that the participation of everyone in the class is not valued. Those students who are not first to answer learn, over time, to stop trying to engage in problem-solving.

Remember to follow questions with a wait time of 15 to 30 seconds. Then ask for many responses, probing students' thinking and facilitating the exchange of ideas.

- *Does everyone agree with this answer? Does anyone disagree? Explain.*
- *Did anyone think about the problem in a different way? Explain.*
- *Tell me more about what you are thinking.*

Dear Reader,

Our math class has been working on theories about odd and even numbers. Please read my theory and its proof and determine, based on the facts I provide you, whether you believe my theory.

Thank you,

_____

• •

Dear Mathematician,

I do/do not believe your theory because (check all relevant statements):

_____ your procedures and examples are clear.

_____ you do not provide adequate examples.

_____ I do not understand your procedures.

_____

_____

_____

Sincerely,

_____

PARAGRAPH FORMAT

Topic Sentence – **Your Theory**

Example **If you** add an odd number to an odd number you will get an even number.

Supportive Sentences – **Procedure**

Example **To prove this** we first built lots of odd numbers with our cubes. When the cubes went together, the odd cubes on top made an even top.

Supporting Sentence – **Examples**

Example **For example,** $3 + 5 = 8$, $5 + 7 = 12$, $3 + 9 = 12$

Concluding Sentence – **Theory Restated**

Example **So we concluded** that if you add any two odd numbers you will always get an even number.

1-CM GRID

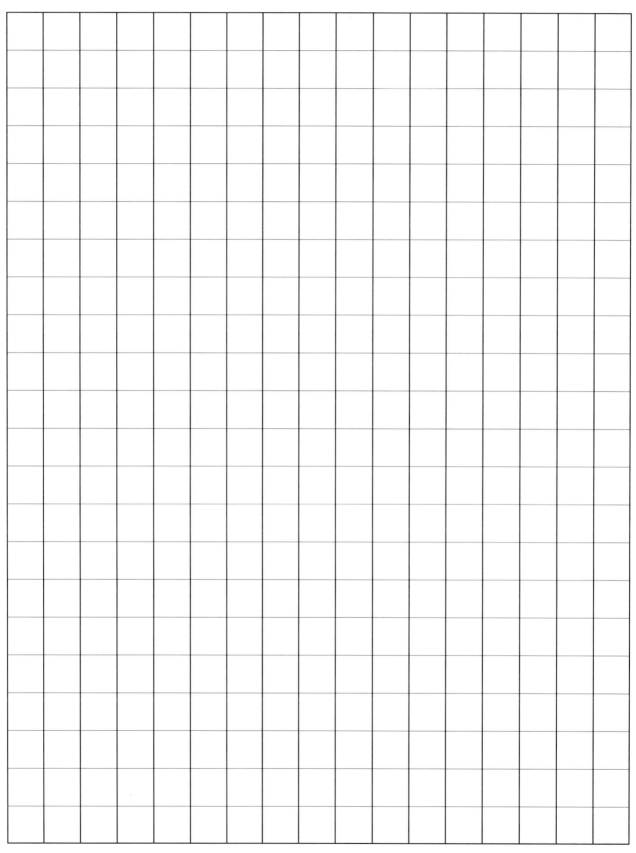

1-INCH GRID

PENTOMINO PUZZLES

1.

Cover each shape with pieces.
Do not cover the shaded part.

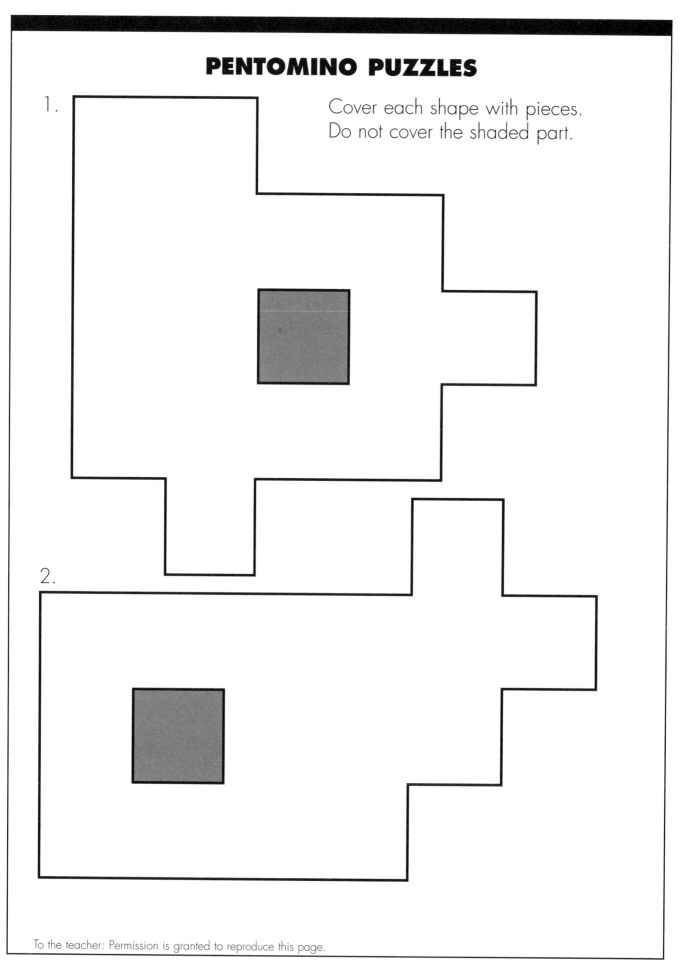

2.

REPORT FORMAT

PARAGRAPH ONE:

General information about the animal

Topic sentence should include the name of the animal and one particularly interesting fact.

Supporting sentences should include some general facts.

PARAGRAPHS TWO THROUGH FIVE:

Each tells specific information about one of the questions.

Topic sentence should tell what the paragraph will be about.

Supporting sentences should give details about the question.

PARAGRAPH SIX:

General summary information

EDITING CHECKLIST

SESSION ONE

Checking for Organization and Readability

• Read your report aloud to yourself.

_____ Does your report have four or five paragraphs?

_____ Does each paragraph have a topic sentence and at least three supporting sentences?

_____ Is your writing easy to read? What changes can you make so it is?

SESSION TWO

Checking for Punctuation and Mechanics

• Read one sentence at a time.

_____ Does every sentence begin with a capital letter?

_____ Does every sentence end with proper punctuation?

_____ Do all your sentences express one clear idea?

SESSION THREE

Checking for Spelling

_____ Circle lightly any words that don't look right.

_____ Use a dictionary to check spelling.

GAME BOARDS

Board A

13	1	26
32	26	19
30	14	17

Board B

4	11	3
5	7	9
8	10	6

Board C

8	7	6
7	7	7
6	7	8

EDITING EXPERTS
ROLES AND QUESTIONS

The Quality Controller looks for quality of thought and content.

- *What suggestions do you have to make the thinking more clear?*
- *What should the writer add or take out to make the writing more interesting?*

The Plumber thinks about the flow of ideas.

- *Does each sentence flow nicely from one thought to the next?*
- *What suggestions do you have for making the paragraph flow more smoothly?*

The Window Wiper thinks about whether the point of the paragraph is clear.

- *What suggestions do you have for making the thinking more clear?*
- *Does the topic sentence tell what the paragraph is about? If not, what suggestions do you have for making the topic sentence more clear?*

The "i" Dotter reads the paragraph for spelling, punctuation, and grammatical errors.

- *Circle lightly any words that don't look right.*
- *Does every sentence express one complete thought and end with the appropriate punctuation?*

To the teacher: Permission is granted to reproduce this page.